)een

your

:nd

t you

ng

something with you to do on holiday.
For many of us it takes a couple of days to get
into the swing of not working and the
activities in this book will ease you in gently.
If you have family you may have to plan or
fight for a relaxing time and this is the perfect
excuse for some quiet moments. Finally,
holidays are an ideal time to discover more
about your journey with God and about your
Creator without the distraction of all those
things that take our time and energy in a
normal day.

The Holiday
Creative Retreat
ACTIVITY BOOK

These pages offer prayers and activities.
Some to challenge and some to help you relax
and clear your mind. Do them at your own
pace and don't undo any good by worrying
that you haven't completed everything. Please
look at the comments at the back of this book
for some additional thoughts and ideas.

With every blessing,

Mary and Mark Fleeson
Holy Island

Sunrise

From the rising of the sun unto the going
down of the same the LORD's name
is to be praised. Psalm 113:3

Get up and watch the sun rise!

Watching the sun rise has to be one of the most
special moments that any of us can experience
but few of us do. If you're on holiday there
shouldn't be the need to get up early or rush
to 'do' anything but the effort will be worth it.

If possible go to the nearest high point half
an hour before sunrise on a morning that is
forecast to be fine. Put any distractions aside
(switch off your phone) and wait.

My soul waits for the Lord more than those
who watch for the morning, more than
those who watch for the morning.
Psalm 130

As you wait be aware of the sense
of anticipation, what does it feel like to wait
for something guaranteed to come?

Prayer

This day, O God, is Yours,
May it be good, May it be right,
May it be filled with Your presence.

This day, O God, is Yours,
May I give freely, May I love unconditionally,
May I hope unreservedly, May I rest in You.

On the opposite page
is a 'focus' activity,
colouring. For a while
leave behind your busy
thoughts, your everyday
concerns and just focus
on the rhythm
of shading.

Invite God to be with you
and enjoy being in the
loving presence
of your Creator.

adore the
Lord your God
he loves you
confess
your sin to him
he forgives you
thank him
for his mercy
he conquered death
surrender
your desires
he is Life

Night

Let nothing disturb you,
nothing frighten you;
all the trials of today will pass,
God never changes!

Wait for and expect God's blessing
if your name is written
on God's hands
you will want for nothing;
God will fulfil your every need.

Adapted from the blessing by St.Teresa of Avila.

It is good to be in constant conversation with God, it is also good
to deliberately set time aside to be with God without distractions.

Sometime our prayers can become like long lists, everything on the list
is important but it can feel like there is no space to just listen to God. One
way of simplifying your prayer time is to limit the number of things you give
to God in any day, make your prayers full of quality rather than quantity
with time to hear what God has to say about them.

Have a go at creating a triune knot by following the stages below or just
darken the lines of the one opposite. ~ Use the knot as springboard into
prayer, represent God in the centre however you want then write three thing
that are one your mind in the remaining spaces. ~ Write a repeating prayer
in the ribbon of the knot (see example below). ~ Follow the knot and repea
the prayer, at each point pause to place whatever is in the space into God's
hands and then wait in silence to see if God wants to tell you something,
if you hear nothing then just be still for a while.

Elevensies

[Martha] had a sister called Mary, who sat at the Lord's feet listening to what He said. Luke 10:39

> Get yourself a hot drink and find somewhere quiet to sit.
>
> Jesus has many things to say to us today but in the busy-ness of life it can be difficult to just stop and listen, most of us are like Martha, over-concerned about keeping all our little juggling balls in the air because we know that if we let them fall it will be even harder to perform later. The story of Mary and Martha isn't suggesting that we drop all our responsibilities, it's about being willing to drop them when God wants us to, it's about being willing to have God change our priorities and focus.

He who is a child of God listens to God's words. John 8:47

> Now, for the next half hour or so try to be a deliberate Mary. Imagine yourself sitting with Jesus. What is He saying to you? What do you most want, or need, to hear today?

Prayer

Jesus I sit at Your feet,
Open my heart to Your presence,
Open my ears to Your words,
Open my mind to the wonder of You.

Sometimes it can be easier to listen to God and to pray if you have something to occupy your hands and distract your mind away from everyday concerns.

Opposite is a technique for using your hands to help your mind to focus.

With a finger from your other hand follow the pattern, doesn't matter where you start. Pray at each point of the 'knot' and where the lines intersect over your palm. You could pray something like this:

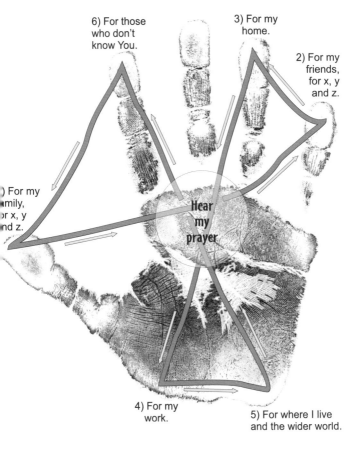

6) For those who don't know You.

3) For my home.

2) For my friends, for x, y and z.

1) For my family, for x, y and z.

Hear my prayer

4) For my work.

5) For where I live and the wider world.

Noon

And He said to them, "Come away by yourselves to a desolate place and rest a while." For many were coming and going, and they had no leisure even to eat.
Mark 6:31 ESV

We were not created to be alone. That doesn't mean that we have to be married or live in community but it does mean that we need social contact to function well as human beings. Deliberately seeking community isn't easy, sometimes it seems impossible, even undesirable, and even if you're surrounded by family it can take an effort to nurture new relationships.

Take time to eat a slow, leisurely meal with others, it could be with family or with new friends if you're holidaying alone. Ban phones and electronic games and make conversation or play old fashioned games. Laugh together.

As your holiday continues think about the communities you are part of, home and family, church, work, etcetera. Do you feel that you are fully immersed in those groups or on the edges? Could you do more to get involved?

Community and communication have the same origin in the Latin for common/shared (communis). How could you use communication to improve your communities? Use the bubbles opposite to jot down your thoughts.

Prayer

Bless the people
I know,
Bless my family,
my friends,
my acquaintances.

May my family
relationships grow
beyond the
boundaries of
obligation,

May my friends feel
that they are family
and may those I
hardly know become
my friends.

Bless the place
where I am,
Bless the places
where I will go.

May I seek
community
and find
You.

my communities

ME

and ideas about them

Sunset

They who dwell in the ends of the earth
stand in awe of Your signs; You make
the dawn and the sunset shout for joy.
Psalm 65:8 NASB

Opposite is a finger labyrinth.
Trace the spiralling path slowly and as you
head towards the centre try to leave your
awareness of the sounds around you and the
bubbling thoughts in your head behind so
that when you reach the middle you are
better able to hear God. When you make
your way back out try to listen for
that 'still, small voice.'

There are many little side paths, try pausing
at them and see what thoughts come into
your head. Pray through those thoughts.

Prayer

As the sun sets on this day
and it comes to an end,
let all that is not of You in me
also end.

As the stars appear
telling of Your vastness,
let all that is of You in me
worship.

Evening

Rejoice always; pray without ceasing; in everything give thanks; for this is God's will for you in Christ Jesus. 1 Thessalonians 5:16-18

We can't physically live without breathing and likewise we can't spiritually live without praying.

When praying becomes like breathing, when we are in continual conversation with God, then we are truly living.

But it isn't easy.

If we go about our everyday business with the awareness of God's presence then we must be prepared to accept that God really does care about our choices, our problems, our joys, our sorrows and our general well-being; that's the lovely warm fuzzy bit. The hard part is then accepting that your needs will be met in God's way, not necessarily your way.

We also have to stop ourselves from becoming hung up about all those nitty-gritty, everyday things that we all do being done in God's sight, I suspect that God, having created us, knows everything about us and doesn't see the small things how we see them.

Our understanding of God will always be limited by our humanity and our humanity will only escape it's confines by imagining without boundaries until we meet our Maker face to face.

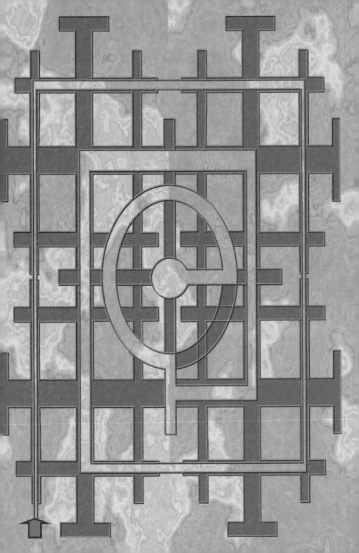

Comments and Encouragements

Take time out. Just ten minutes a day or half an hour twice a week set aside purely for being in God's presence can make a big difference to how your spiritual life grows. Find a quiet place and give the time you have to God, you could use the prayer in the Sunrise section of this book.

Pray like it's as vital as breathing. Sometimes we place praying, like God, into box. We think God can only be met or talked to in Church or when a certain person is present, in reality we were created to communicate with our Creator, to enjoy a two-way conversation which never ends. There's so much God wants to share with us, to show us and teach us, so pray constantly and be aware of Gods presence in all things.

Look for God in the small things. The snatched conversation you just had with the shop assistant, God was there; the hug you gave your grieving friend, God was there; the moment you took to smell the flowers, God was there; when you washed up after dinner, God was there. It isn't that God wants to do the washing up for you or promise you that every washing up moment will be filled with joy but God may be telling you that if you spend those times that need little thought, in prayer and conversation with your Creator, then your life may be that bit richer and purposeful.

I should point out that if you don't pray during the washing up your life will not fall apart, I know that sometimes I'm so tired that I can't even form a coherent thought let alone pray sensibly and a few minutes of mindless washing up is a pleasurable chance to switch off. If you can't pray then try singing or humming and just be open to whatever God may want to say to you.

Never 'beat yourself up' for not doing enough, practice just being and be available when God calls you to do something.

Allow yourself to be vulnerable to others and to God. It's not easy to do but when we allow others to see our true selves they will see more of God and God will be able to use you more effectively to help others.

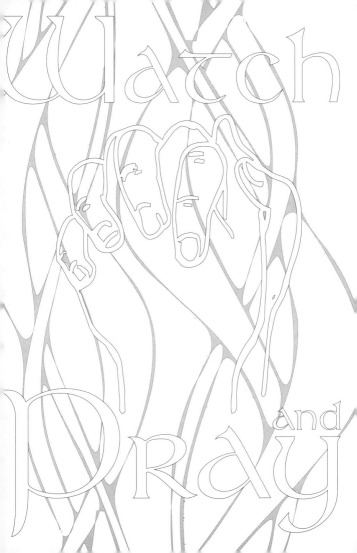

Midnight

Watch and pray, that ye enter not into temptation: the spirit indeed is willing, but the flesh is weak. Matthew 26:41

For one night only of your holiday stay up really late!

You may consider a Vigil to be something you do only at Easter, Christmas, Pentecost or perhaps as a mark of respect or protest but a solitary Vigil, at a time when it is unlikely that you will be disturbed (and when you can easily catch up your sleep after) can be a good way to listen to God and rest in His presence.

Find a quiet place with subdued lighting and light a single candle.

Whenever you find your thoughts drifting onto more mundane things focus on the candle, be aware of how the light pulses and flickers and how it gently pushes away the darkness.

Listen to the silence and let it envelop you like a warm blanket.

Additional note:
You may be fed up of quiet and stillness, perhaps you've had one too many sleepless nights, if that is you then try using a candle to help you focus at another time and have some appropriate music playing, or invite a friend or two to join you and pray together.

Prayer

In the darkness
our souls cry out.
Do You hear?

In the stillness
our hearts weep.
Do You care?

1 John 5:14-15
...God listens to us if we ask for anything that has His approval. We know that He listens to our requests. So we know that we already have what we ask Him for.

When we cry out
at injustice,
at cruelty
and wrong,
Hear our prayer.

When we weep
with the lost,
the lonely,
the poor,
Hear our prayer.